To all the children, parents & grandparents

wherever they are.

Acknowledgment

To all my very much loved family in Israel and England who support me in everything I do and without whom this book would not have been possible. To my children and to my husband Rob, who not only did a great job of taking the photographs as well as preparing the technical side of the book, but who is a great support to me and an endless source of love.

Many thanks also to all my friends who helped and supported me throughout the long birthing process of this project.

Baby Massage

BABY MASSAGE

A Comprehensive Step - by - Step Guide

Written by **Galit Hughes**

Photo's by **Rob Hughes**

Published in the UK by Shunyata
27 Hamsey Road, Sharpthorne, W. Sussex, RH19 4PA
www.shunyata.co.uk
Galit@shunyata.co.uk

Published in Israel by Ya'ar, book publishers
Flory@barak.net.co.il

ISBN   0 - 9540143 - 0 - 8

A catalogue record of this book is available from the British Library

Translated from Hebrew by Sari Avis
Edited by Ivor & Barbara Hughes and Diane Jones
Photography by Rob Hughes

Art design by Sarit Zeltzer
Cover design by Sarit Zeltzer
syzeltzer@lineone.net

Printed in the UK by Nuffield Press

Printed on paper from sustainable forests

All the techniques shown in this book have been used safely by the authors for many years. Many other parents and babies have also enjoyed their therapeutic effects. The information provided is used at the reader's own choice and risk. If in doubt always ask for professional advice from your doctor, midwife or baby massage instructor.

CONTENTS

Why Massage Babies? Massage and Energy Circulation, When Should I Start? Fathers and Massage, When to Avoid Massage, Preparing for the Massage

Preparation, Lavender Oil, Geranium Oil, Chamomile Oil, Recommended Blend for Massaging Babies

Coughs, Colds, Bronchitis & Blocked Sinuses, Colic Pain, Wind & Constipation, Teething, Relaxation & Improving Sleep

Stroking, Tapping

From the Abdomen to the Hands, From the Abdomen to the Legs

Opening the Chest, Tapping on the Chest

Pressing & Stretching the Arms, Stroking the Arms, The Hands

Forward

One of the most basic human urges towards one we love is to touch, stroke and hold. When we touch we transfer love, care and feeling, a gentle touch and quiet murmur can calm and reassure.

From conception to birth your child is enveloped in a warm, safe and rhythmic environment, comfortable and secure.

For the first nine months of life a child is massaged by the rhythmic contractions of the womb and the motion of the mother's body. With the help of this book you can gain the confidence to transfer this comfort through your touch.

Massaging your baby from birth onwards will enable you to bring peace and harmony for both yourself and your child, building a positive and harmonious relationship that will follow through in other aspects of your parenting patterns.

Claudia Levi RGN RHV

Health Visitor

Why Massage Babies?

For centuries families in the Far East have used massage as an important means of maintaining good health. In these cultures massage is considered one of the principal means of strengthening the body and preventing disease.

Mothers in India, Nepal, and now increasingly in the West, massage their babies and children every day as part of their childcare routine. In Eastern countries this skill is commonplace and massage techniques are often passed on from mother to daughter. In the West however, despite growing interest, massage is still considered a luxury. Many still believe that people who receive a massage are merely spoiling themselves. They are unable to appreciate that massage can in fact be one of the keys to a happy and healthy life.

For the whole family, massage is a gentle and effective way of treating both physical and mental problems. The advantage of massage is that it is enjoyable and healing, while at the same time it fulfills one of the most fundamental human needs; namely touch.

Caring human touch revitalises self-confidence and restores calmness: it both relaxes and heals. Each one of us, at any age, can benefit greatly from it. Massage given by a family member (parents to children, children to parents, a couple to each other) is a source of companionship, love, warmth and intimacy; it also has a strong positive influence on family relations.

The physical touch of massage encourages good blood circulation, relaxes muscles and nerves, improves the functioning of the lymphatic system (and the immune system), and has a relaxing effect on the mind. Massage both invigorates and improves the functioning of all the body's systems, furthermore, it leaves us with a fresh, light, and pleasant feeling inside.

By encouraging relaxation, our internal organs function better and as a consequence our health is also improved. Massage helps us to experience the truth of the phrase "a healthy mind in a healthy body".

Tension, restlessness, and irritability are one of the main causes of disease, hence the importance of the calming effect of massage in the maintenance of health. Reasons for restlessness in babies are different to those in adults. A baby who is left on his own in a cot for a long time will become restless and unhappy. This can be expressed through incessant crying, which could cause or worsen digestive problems and produce wind and stomach ache.

Babies need physical touch during most of the day. Physical contact with the mother, father, or another caring person, is a natural follow-on to the cradling and nurturing experienced in the womb. Physical contact gives the baby confidence and relaxes him. Unfortunately our lifestyle in the Western world restricts parents from carrying their babies close to them at all times. Many babies lack the physical contact that is necessary for their development. Daily massage is a good way to compensate for the lack of physical contact between parents and their children. In so doing you will be spending an intimate and special time together, getting to know each other better and developing mutual confidence and trust in each other.

Parents of both premature babies and those suffering from specific problems such as hyperactivity, sensory/motor problems and Down's syndrome will also discover that massage is a rewarding way to spend time with their child. Both parent & child become closer and grow to know each other more, plus the parent is enabled to support the baby's physical, emotional & mental growth. This way, parents will discover that they, too, can enhance and support the child's development, rather than leaving all the care in the hands of the professionals.

Massage and Energy Circulation

Massage has a direct effect on the body's circulation of energy. Traditional Chinese Medicine works by treating the flow of energy in the body, known as the "meridian system." The meridian system is a complex network of energy, supporting and connecting the internal organs and body systems in a continuous and dynamic circulation. The effective flow of this energy is directly related to our health. When the energy flows freely,

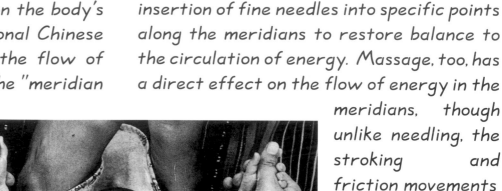

it manifests in the proper functioning of the body's systems and internal organs. A blockage in one of the meridians will in time manifest as pain and/or disease; the immune system can become weakened, negative changes of mood may occur, and tension and nervousness will often be felt.

The Chinese system of Acupuncture uses this philosophy and is administered by the insertion of fine needles into specific points along the meridians to restore balance to the circulation of energy. Massage, too, has a direct effect on the flow of energy in the meridians, though unlike needling, the stroking and friction movements affect the whole length of the meridians rather than focussing on specific points. Massage releases the flow of energy in the meridians, removes blockages, and so encourages the circulation of energy in the body. Regular massage can prevent illness, strengthen the body and improve its functioning, and where there is disease, help and promote recovery.

When should I Start?

It is good to start massaging your baby as soon after the birth as possible. If you choose to give your baby his first massage immediately after the birth, care should be taken with the area around the navel, only massaging this area gently until the remains of the umbilical cord are completely detached.

Start massaging gradually by spreading the oil on the baby's skin using light, soft strokes. Massage whilst cradling the baby in your arms or when breast feeding him. When he has got used to the feeling of being massaged, you can start using the massage routines in this book. For the first week about 5-10 minutes a day will be enough; as time goes on increase the length of the massage depending on the response from your baby. He will enjoy the sensation of being naked and will come to welcome the daily massage with a wide smile. Starting gradually is particularly important for newborns, e.g. babies less than a month old, and for premature babies.

When the baby's movements are more free, and he begins to turn over and crawl, it becomes harder to continue the daily routine of full body massage. At this time it is worthwhile sticking to the gym and play exercises in the chapter on "Baby Gymnastics".

If the baby has older brothers or sisters, it is likely that they will show an interest in the massage. They may ask to take part in giving the massage, or even to receive a massage themselves. This is a great opportunity to allow them an active part in caring for the baby, or to enjoy a similar experience themselves.

Fathers and Massage

In the early months after the baby's birth, many fathers feel distanced and disconnected from the experience of caring for their child. Most of the day the baby sleeps, and the main activity while awake, namely breast-feeding, is carried out by the mother. Massaging the baby is a pleasant way for the father to get to know his baby and to feel that he, too, is involved in caring for him. During the massage, an intimate and special bond is created between father and baby, similar in quality to that created between mother and baby during breast-feeding.

When to Avoid Massage

Do not wake the baby for massage and never massage a baby against her will. Do not insist forcefully on using strokes she objects to. Stop the massage if the baby is crying and calm her down. Only continue massaging when she is fully relaxed again. If you wish to continue massaging after the baby has started crawling and sitting up, do so only when she is receptive.

If the baby has received an inoculation, it is advisable to wait at least a day until she feels better, and only then resume the massage routine. Avoid touching the area of the injection until fully healed (about a week). In case of rashes, fever, or inflammation, it is important to take extra care and consult a GP before massaging the baby.

Preparing for the Massage

Approach the massage feeling comfortable and self-assured. Only this way will the baby feel safe and relaxed. If you are hesitant or uncertain, the baby will feel it immediately. To avoid a lack of confidence, you can practice the strokes on a partner, doll, or yourself. When you feel you have mastered the strokes, you can try them on the baby. The baby may cry for the first few massages. This is common and natural for new born and premature babies and should not deter you from continuing. If this happens stop the massage to calm your baby down and continue only if he is happy to do so. It is important that the massage is associated with pleasure for both him and for you.

It is equally important for you to feel physically comfortable while giving a massage. Your body, arms, and back should be relaxed. It is possible to give a massage standing up, while the baby lies on a changing bed or any other table. It is also possible to be sitting with your legs stretched out in front of you and the baby lying on top of them. Alternatively this can be done on a soft, comfortable blanket on the floor. Weather permitting, it can even be pleasurable to be outdoors. Whether you are inside or out, make sure that the baby is warm enough when naked. You can put on some relaxing music and turn on the answer-phone, (so as not to interrupt a massage with continuous phone calls). Whatever environment or position you choose, the most important thing is to feel comfortable and relaxed.

Evening is a good time to give a massage, before bathing the baby and preparing him for sleep. This will lead the baby into a relaxing, quiet night's sleep. However, it is possible to adjust massage time as you wish according to the baby's daily routines; his meal, rest, play and bath-times. It is important not to massage the baby when he is too tired or too hungry. If you choose to massage the baby after a meal, it is better to wait for about half an hour.

Preparation

Massage oils can be divided into two kinds: carrier oils and essential oils. Carrier oils are natural plant oils. Preferably they should be cold-pressed, as this method preserves the vitamins and minerals necessary to nourish the skin. Two highly recommended carrier oils for baby massage are grapeseed oil and almond oil. Both are gentle, pleasant and odourless, and are therefore especially suitable for the baby's delicate skin. Any other natural oil is acceptable including olive, sesame, coconut and sunflower oils. Most baby oils sold in pharmacies are synthetic, petro-chemical by-product oils. They do not nourish or protect the skin, moreover they may block-up the pores, prevent the skin from breathing freely and toxic residues may be absorbed. To the carrier oil a choice of essential oils is added. Essential oils are very strong concentrates produced from particular parts of different plants i.e. their flowers, leaves, roots, seeds, or stems. Essential oils have many healing properties:

some are disinfectant, some are useful for colds, coughs and inflammations, others help to strengthen the immune system and are good for skin conditions or have a calming effect on the mind. Essential oils influence the body in two ways: by direct contact and therefore absorption through the skin; and through inhaling the vapour which influences the nervous system.

Before using the massage oil you have prepared, you must be sure that the baby is not allergic to these oils. Put a little of the oil on a small area of the baby's body and wait for 30 minutes. If any redness appears on the skin, try using a different combination of carrier and essential oils. If in doubt, consult an aromatherapist.

Remember: essential oils are very concentrated and strong. Do not under any circumstances use them directly on the skin, or drink them. Also do not use essential oils at a more concentrated dilution than recommended.

To prepare massage oil for babies of two months or less, the ratio should be 1-3 drops of essential oil to every 30 ml. carrier oil. For babies over two months, 3-5 drops of essential oils can be used to every 30 ml. carrier oil. It is preferable to prepare the oils in a bottle in advance, so it is ready for the next few massages. The oil should be stored in a dark glass bottle and kept in a cool place; this way it will not deteriorate and lose its healing properties as quickly. Essential oils are not only useful for massaging babies, but also for yourself, as well as for treating pets and even plants. They can be purchased in health food shops or directly from the many companies who now stock them. Below are listed three suitable essential oils for babies; lavender, geranium and chamomile oil.

Lavender oil

Lavender oil has many uses: it has antiseptic properties, is useful for disinfecting wounds, strengthens the immune system, clears toxins, prevents inflammation, helps heal wounds, and is especially beneficial for burns. Lavender is used in the treatment of rashes, and for babies is especially useful for nappy rash. Lavender oil has a relaxing effect on the mind, which makes it very effective for treating irritable babies, who cry a lot. It also helps induce sleep.

Geranium oil

Geranium is an oil with a pleasant smell and a calming influence on the nervous system, therefore very useful for more restless babies and those who do not sleep well. It nourishes the skin and is therefore suitable for a baby's delicate skin.

Chamomile oil

Chamomile oil is antibacterial, disinfectant and predominantly anti-inflammatory.

While chamomile tea is very beneficial for internal inflammations, external inflammations are also treated with chamomile essential oil. Burns, eczema, asthma, diarrhoea, nausea, psoriasis and fever are successfully treated with Chamomile. Due to its effect on the nervous system it is also beneficial in the treatment of irritable babies.

Recommended Blend for Massaging Babies

Use 30 ml carrier oil of your choice, with the addition of:

* 1 drop of lavender oil
* 1 drop of geranium oil
* 1 drop of chamomile oil.

Or alternatively a total of 3 drops of one or two of the above.

Once you start giving your baby a full body massage regularly, both the body and the immune system will strengthen and your baby's chance of becoming ill will decrease. In the event that she does get sick, she will recover more quickly and easily as a result of a strengthened immune system.

When babies get sick and are suffering from pain or discomfort (eg. an earache or stomach ache) the body becomes contracted and tense and they become anxious. This atmosphere of tension very often prevents the body from healing. Drug therapy may prevent inflammations and infections, but massage often "nips the problem in the bud", by relaxing the body and stimulating the functioning of the different bodily systems, thereby helping babies to heal themselves.

When considering how to massage a sick baby or child, it is important to draw on your previous experience in massaging. This is not to say that you need to be a professional masseuse to treat a sick child,

but you do need the benefits of previous experience in order to deliver the massage strokes with confidence and in a relaxed way, so that the baby will become relaxed and peaceful.

You will find detailed below some of the most common problems found in babies and children, accompanied by a description of how to treat them using massage. _Please remember, if your baby has a high fever and is very unwell, do consult with your GP._

Coughs, Colds, Bronchitis & Blocked Sinuses

To treat cold, coughs and bronchitis, prepare a massage oil from 2tbs of carrier oil, 1 drop each of lavender. eucalyptus and ginger essential oils. Massage the mixture into the baby's chest and upper back, as shown in the appropriate chapters. Repeat three times a day for a few minutes each time. When the baby is over a year, use two drops of each of the above essential oils for the same amount of carrier oil. In the case of a cold accompanied by a blocked nose, use less of the same mixture, to give your baby a face massage (being careful to avoid the eyes). Also use this oil to massage the whole of the baby's body.

The diet of a breast-feeding mother or the baby's own diet once weaned has a strong influence on the functioning of her respiratory system, especially where there are breathing problems related to phlegm; bronchitis and chronic colds etc. Dairy products, fried foods, chocolate, red meat, oranges, bananas, and peanuts all increase mucous in the body and are better avoided by both mother and baby.

Colic Pain, Wind and Constipation

Massage the abdomen as detailed in the chapter on the abdominal massage at least once a day as part of the whole body massage routine. It can take a week or two before there will be a significant change or until the problem is truly under control. You can also use the strokes on the abdomen through clothing whenever you feel your baby experience discomfort.

In order to help a baby release wind, bring her knees to her chest holding them together, and press down her tummy (see picture on page 84-85). The wind will be released and the baby will feel immediate relief!

When a baby is ill or in pain, the parents are put under a lot of stress. The ensuing long, sleepless nights add greatly to both the baby's and the parents' irritability, making the situation all the worse. Try to relax and make up for lost sleep during the day while your baby is asleep. Massage will not only relieve the baby's colic pain, but will also allow you some quiet, relaxed time together.

Being able to help your baby and reduce her suffering gives you a sense of security, and adds a great deal to the well-being of the baby.

Whilst breast feeding, certain habits and foods can adversely affect the baby's health. For instance, stomach-aches and wind problems are more common in babies whose mothers either smoke, drink a lot of caffeine or consume too many dairy products. Eating legumes (pulses), cauliflower, cabbage and spicy foods can also contribute to your baby's colic problems. Try to watch the effects of the foods you are eating on your baby. Every baby is sensitive to different foods and only you can detect what it is in your diet that is upsetting her.

Teething

Pain caused by teething is treated by massaging the baby's gums from the outside (see picture on page 75). A blend of 1 tablespoon of carrier oil with 2 drops of chamomile essential oil is recommended.

Also, try giving your baby chamomile tea when she starts eating solids. It will have a calming and soothing effect on her and will help relieve the pain.

Relaxation & Improving Sleep

The touch of massage, the quiet time shared by parent and baby, the positive/relaxing effect of the massage on your baby's muscles and nervous system, the healing effect of the oils: all fill your baby with confidence, tranquillity, and a sense of comfort. As a rule, when the massage strokes flow downwards from the upper body to the hands and feet, the effect will be relaxing. When stroking in the opposite direction, from the hands and feet up towards the head, the effect of the massage is more stimulating. However babies are likely to be tired and fall into a deep and long sleep after a massage and a warm bath.

Many babies are restless at particular times of the day, most commonly between 6.00pm and 10.00 pm. It is preferable therefore, to give the baby a massage prior to this time, when they are more ready to receive it. With time, the baby will become calm and relaxed during those hours previously considered 'difficult'.

The Massage Strokes

The massage strokes are simple and easy to learn in a short time. They develop intuitively, and naturally become personalised. A precise order is not important. What is important however is to keep the movement flowing, and to maintain hand contact with the baby's skin as well as eye contact with the baby where possible. Repeat each stroke at least five times. If the baby especially likes some of the strokes, you can repeat them more often. Any strokes he doesn't enjoy, can be skipped and then returned to a few days later.

muscles, and internal organs, as well as the circulatory, nervous, lymph, energy and digestive systems. Therefore whenever the word "stroke" is used, remember to aim for a stronger pressure than that used in everyday touch.

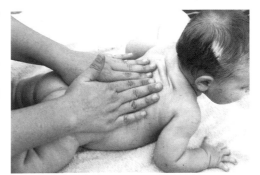

Stroking

The primary massage movement is achieved by stroking your baby's skin with the palms of your hands. The feel of this stroke should be stronger and deeper than an ordinary everyday stroke of affection. In this way it is able to affect not only the surface of the skin, but also reach the

Tapping

The second movement that is used is tapping. This is mainly carried out on the chest and back. It is done with the fingertips, or a cupped hand.

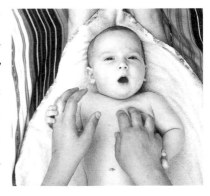

Equipment for the Massage

Before starting the massage make sure you have all you need to hand:

* A large towel, on which the baby will lie.
* A cloth nappy or a small towel, to absorb urine.
* Massage oil, in a small bowl.
* A few of the baby's favourite toys, to keep him busy especially when he gets bigger and starts to move around more.
* A heater, if the room is cold.
* Music that you and your baby like (optional).

Beginning

Before commencing the massage, find the most comfortable position for you and your baby. Make sure your arms and back are relaxed, and that all you will need is to hand.

Begin by pouring a little of the massage oil into your palms, warming it by rubbing your hands together. The first two sequences described below are a convenient way of spreading the oil onto the baby's skin. Alternate these two sequences about five times each, in a slow, constant rhythm, letting the baby get used to the touch of your hands. Both sequences connect the baby's upper body with his lower, making them feel especially pleasant. Return to them once or twice, whenever you finish massaging a specific area of the baby's body.

From the Abdomen to the Palms of the Hands

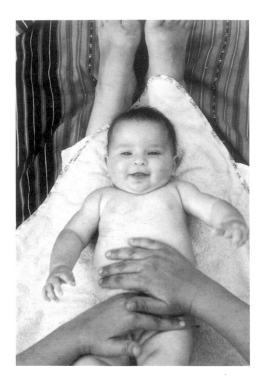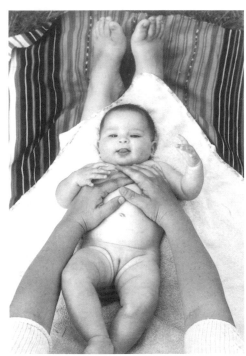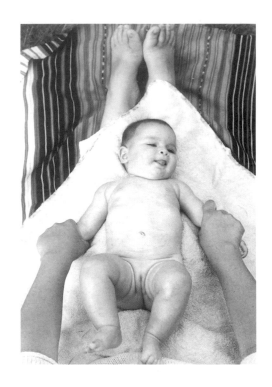

Slide your palms from the lower abdomen (under the belly button) up towards the baby's chest and down along the arms to the fingertips.

Remember - it is important to keep a slow and steady pace when you run your palms down along the baby's arms. Straighten and pull the arms gently. Incorporate this movement with the next, (`from the abdomen to the feet') and repeat them both about four times.

From the Abdomen to the Feet

 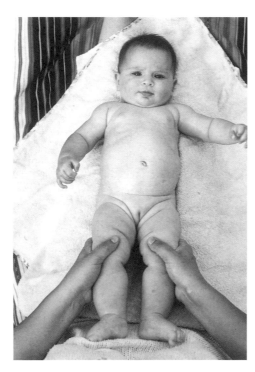 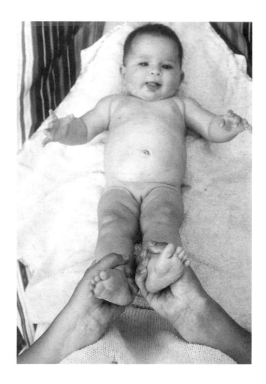

Again, slide your palms from under the belly button, upwards towards the chest, and this time, down along the sides of the body to the legs and feet.

While stroking your palms along your baby's legs, stretch them gently towards you.

The Chest

To ensure deep and gentle breathing, the chest has to be relaxed and free. The ribs protect the heart and lungs. They are made up of 108 tiny joints and many muscles supporting them. The flexibility of the muscles and joints allow the lungs to contain a large quantity of oxygen - vital for life and energy. The heart pumps and transports oxygen through the blood to every cell in the body. Massage relaxes the chest muscles and increases lung capacity, deepening the breathing and allowing the free flow of blood and energy in the whole area thereby improving the functioning of the heart.

Opening the Chest

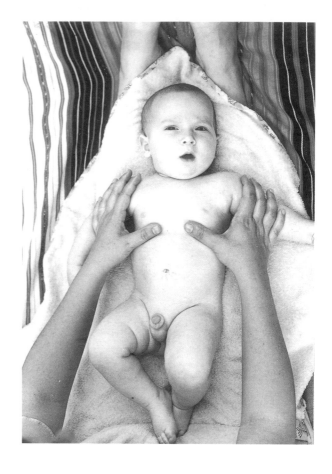

Put your palms on the centre of the baby's chest. Slide them out to the sides, as if trying to flatten pages of an open book. Repeat about five times

Place your fingers on your baby's shoulders. Slide your thumbs from the centre of the chest outwards, following the spaces between the ribs (the intercostal muscles).

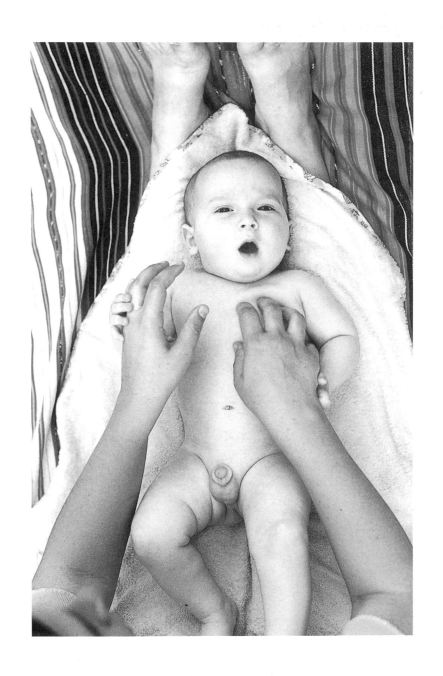

Tapping on the Chest

With the tips of your fingers tap gently on the baby's chest until you hear an echo. Alternate fairly rapidly from one hand to the other.

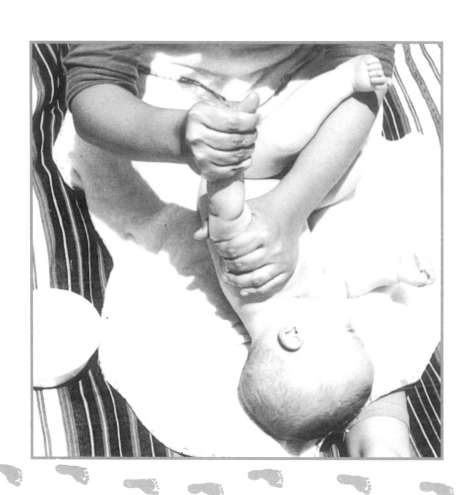

The Arms & Hands

The arms and hands have great importance in the development of co-ordination and learning in your baby. In the first two months of life, the baby will strengthen his arms by waving them in the air and by attempting to raise himself up when lying on his front. Later, as his co-ordination evolves, he will be able to crawl, raise himself up fully, and use his arms for balancing while sitting, standing, and walking.

The arms and hands are the principal tools of our most developed sense - namely the sense of touch. The baby uses them to learn about and communicate with the world around him. He learns to hold his toys and other objects, and later on to use them for more advanced tasks. He learns to point to objects, to reach out to touch and feel your face, or to wave his arms when he wants to be picked up.

Massaging your baby's arms and hands will improve general dexterity, facilitating co-ordination, strengthening shoulder joints, elbows, and wrists, as well as relaxing muscles.

Pressing & Stretching the Arms

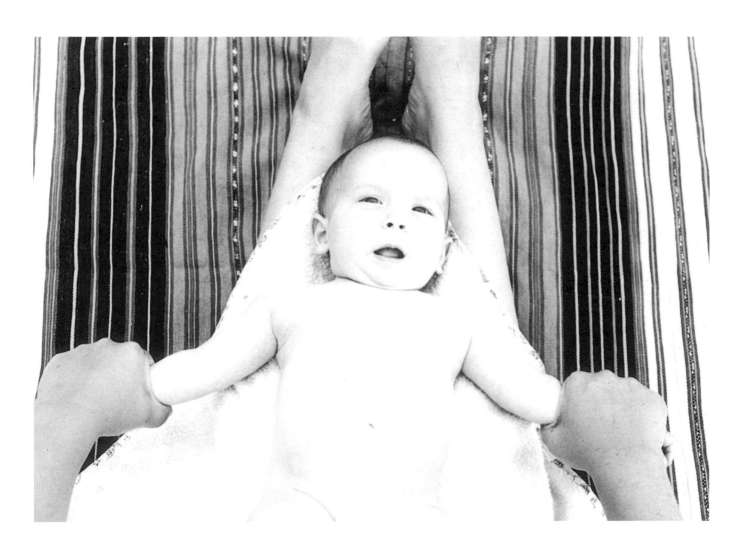

Circle the baby's arms with your thumb and index fingers close to the shoulders and advance your hands towards the wrists pressing lightly. While pressing, straighten and stretch the arms gently. Repeat about five times.

Stroking the Arms

Massage each arm separately, with a gentle stretching movement. Slide hands along the baby's arm as if climbing a rope. One hand slides along the outer side of the arm, from the shoulder to the wrist, and the other along the inner side, from the arm pit to the wrist. Use some pressure on the arm, so the stroke will have an effect on the muscles too. Don't forget to massage the other arm!

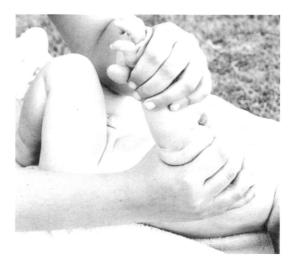

The Hands

With your thumbs, gently open the baby's fist as if flattening a ball of dough, and stroke the palm with circular movements.

With one hand hold the baby's wrist, and with the other 'squeeze' each finger in turn, while sliding your fingers all the way to the tips of the nails.

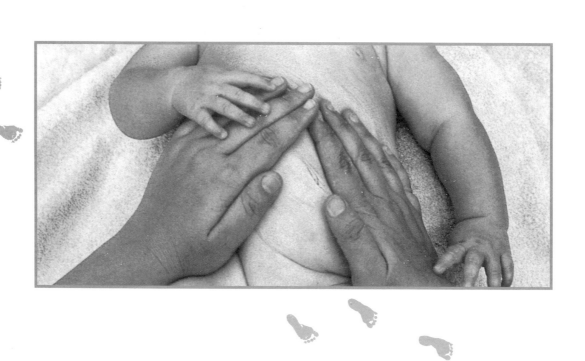

The Abdomen

In Chinese medicine the abdomen is considered one of the body's principal energy centres. We think with our head, feel with our heart, and sense with our abdomen ('gut feeling'). Tension, fear, and anxiety contract the abdomen, while peace, calm and love relax it. The abdomen is home to the internal organs: liver, spleen, stomach, intestines, bladder and kidneys. These organs will benefit greatly from massage as it will gently stimulate their function. If the abdominal muscles are relaxed, breathing is deeper. Babies who suffer from constipation, wind or stomach-ache, will have their problem quickly relieved, if receiving abdominal massage daily.

For abdominal massage to be relaxing and truly beneficial for the digestive system it is important to massage especially slowly and at a constant pace. As you continue, gradually increase pressure on the abdomen. Always massage the abdomen in a clockwise direction. This is the direction of the intestinal flow.

Hearts on the Abdomen

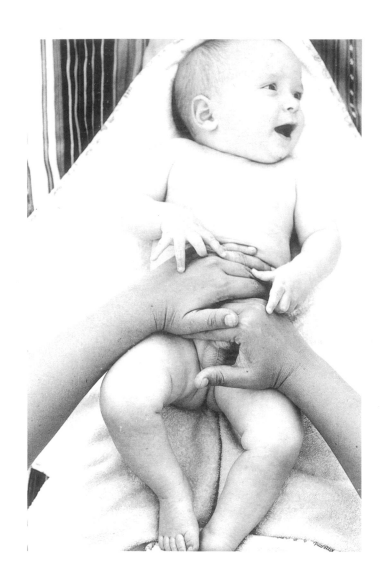

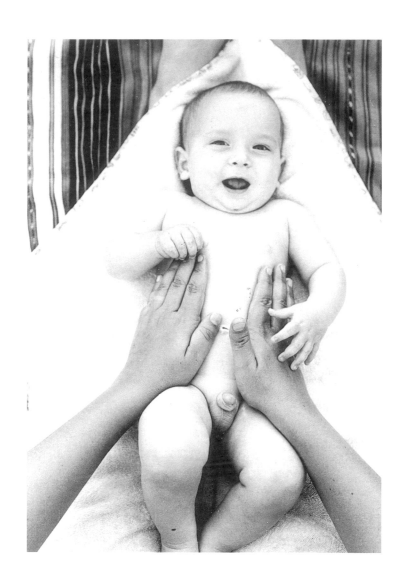

Place your hands on your baby's lower abdomen. Slide your hands upward to the lower ribs.

Separate your hands outwards and slide them down along the sides of the abdomen.

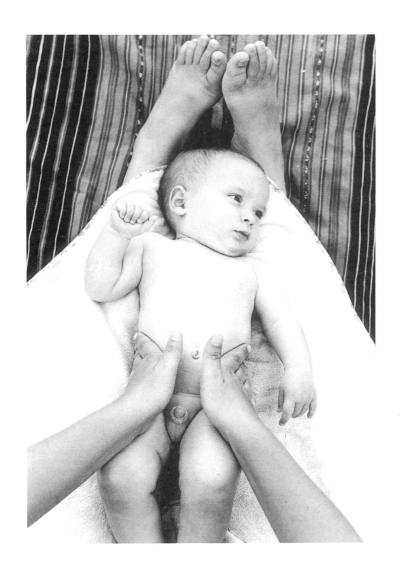 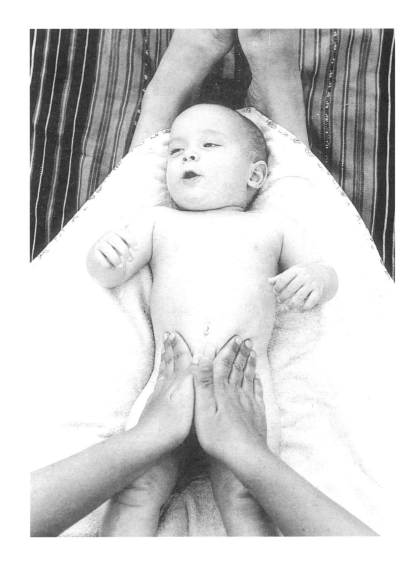

Complete the movement just under the navel.

Gradually increase the pressure on the sides of the abdomen. The movement creates a heart shape on the baby's abdomen. Repeat the sequence about five times.

Clockwise Circles Around the Navel

Place your right hand above and your left hand below the navel. Slide your hands around the navel in a clockwise direction. Your left hand should complete a full circle, from the lower abdomen, round and back, while the right hand moves through only half a circle, from above the navel clockwise as far as the lower abdomen and back again, crossing over the left hand.

This is a continuous circular movement. Slowly increase the pressure on the abdomen. Repeat the circle about ten times, in a slow and unified rhythm.

If the baby suffers from wind or constipation this movement can be repeated as often as needed.

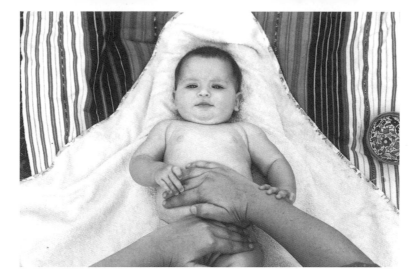

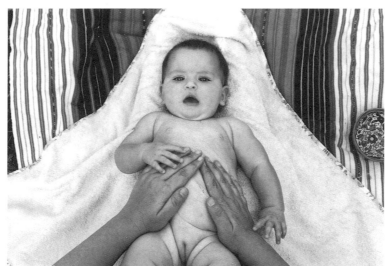

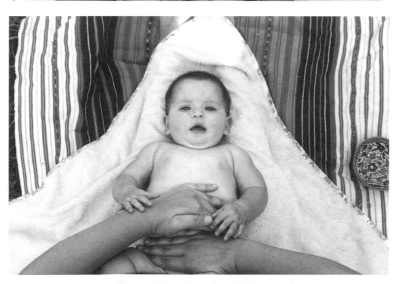

From the Abdomen to the Back

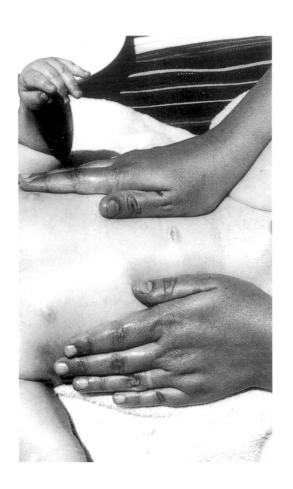 

Place your hands on both sides of the navel, and slide them out to the sides so that your fingers meet at the baby's back, on his spine. Pull your hands to the sides and up, so that the baby's lower back will arch a little. Repeat about five times.

Down the Front of the Body

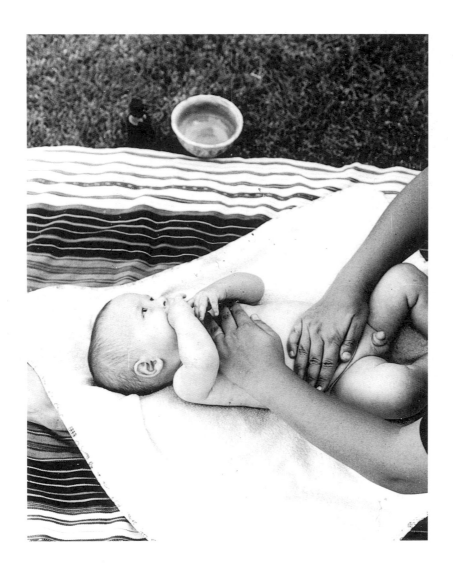

Slide your hands down the front of the baby's body, one hand following after the other.

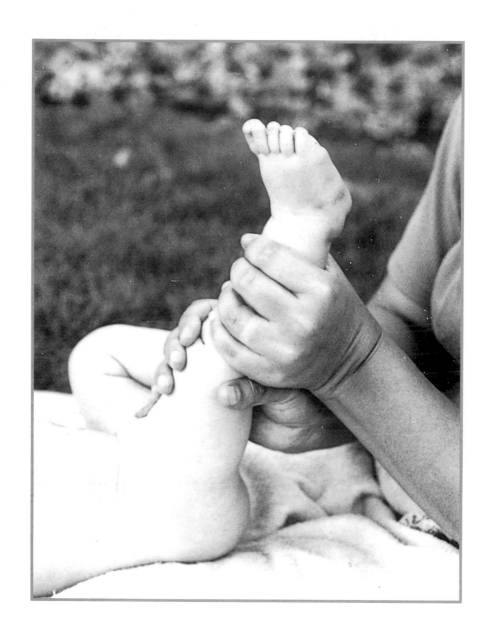

The Legs and Feet

The legs and feet are the foundation of the whole body, and should therefore be strong in order to be supportive. They should also be supple to enable light movement. In the first few months of life, the baby kicks in the air and so strengthens his leg muscles, as well as the ankle, knee, and hip joints. Crawling, sitting and standing are all stages in the process of strengthening the legs, thus enabling the baby to walk. The ability to balance is an integral part of this development. Massaging the legs will relax muscles, strengthen joints and improve co-ordination.

In the therapy of reflexology the feet are considered to be a map of the whole body: with this in mind, one can see how sensitively applied foot massage benefits the whole body. Through the feet, it is possible to influence all areas of the body as well as the internal organs.

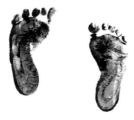

Stretching the Legs

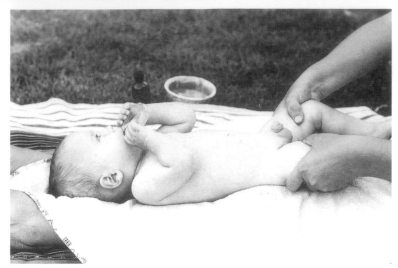

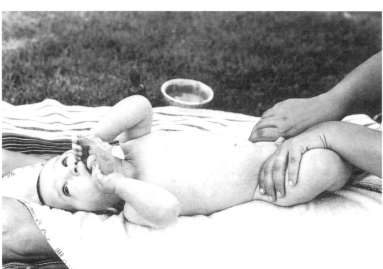

Place your hands on the upper part of the inner thighs. Slide them out to the baby's outer thighs and down to the feet. While sliding your hands down the legs stretch them and straighten them towards you.

Massaging the Thighs

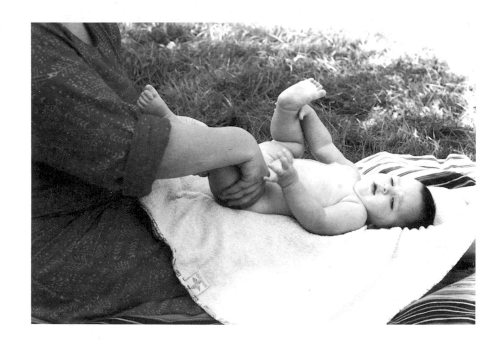

Hold the baby's ankle with your left hand while placing your right hand on his inner thigh.

Slide the right hand round to the outer thigh, and then without losing contact with the skin, slide it back round to its starting point.

Repeat this movement about ten times, in a fast and regular rhythm.

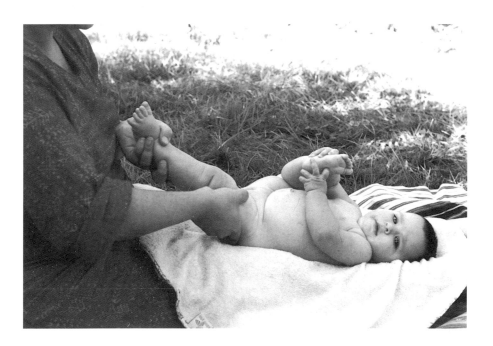

Stroking down the Legs

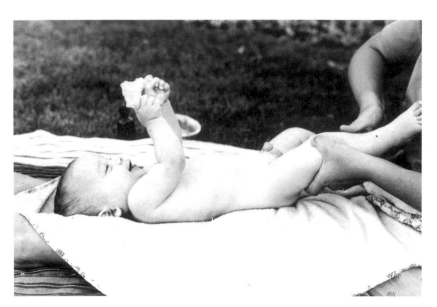 

This movement is identical to the stretching movement described for the arms 'Stroking the Arm's.

With one hand hold the baby's leg close to the hip joint, and in the other hold his ankle. Slide your hand down the leg, as if climbing a rope. One hand slides down the outer thigh and lower leg, and the other hand slides down the inner thigh and lower leg.

Use the same movement for the other leg.

Massaging the Legs with a Corkscrew Motion

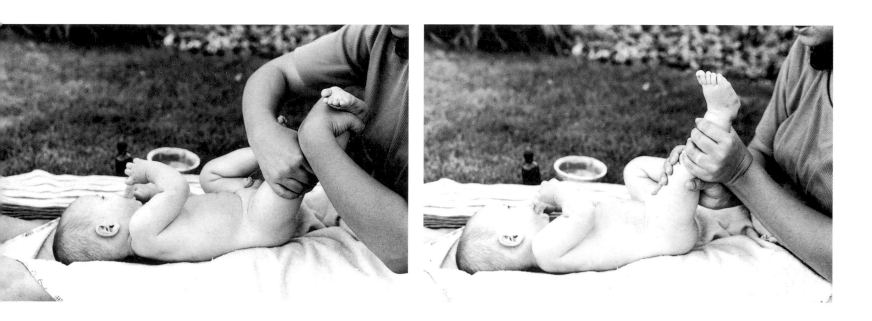

Hold one of the baby's legs on either side with both hands. Slide the palms of your hands round, towards each other and then away from each other, similar to following the grooves of a corkscrew, from the thigh to the ankle. Repeat about three times on each leg.

Stroking the Backs of the Legs & Buttocks

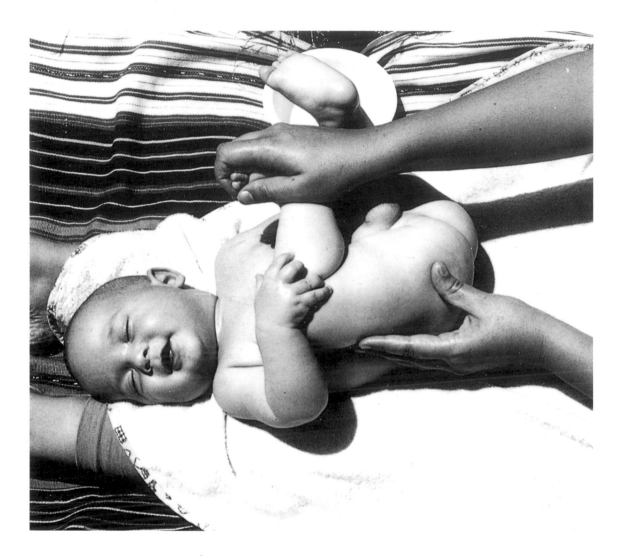

With one hand hold the baby's foot and bring it close to his abdomen with the knee falling to the side. With the thumb of your free hand, massage the back of the thigh and the buttock, in circular movements. Repeat this on the other side.

The Feet

Hold the baby's ankle and with the thumb of the other hand massage the foot in circular motions.

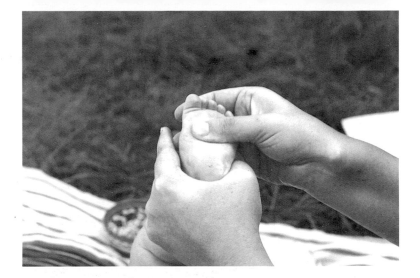

Hold the baby's ankle and with the thumb of the other hand slide and press along the top of the foot, in the spaces between the bones and toes (metatarsal bones). The direction of the movement is from the ankle to the toes.

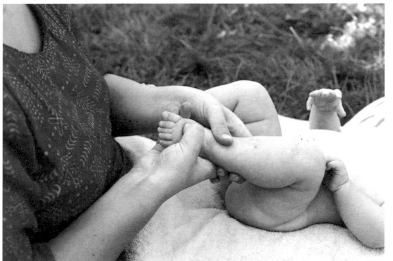

With one hand hold the baby's ankle and with the other gently pull and stretch each toe to the tips of the nails.

53

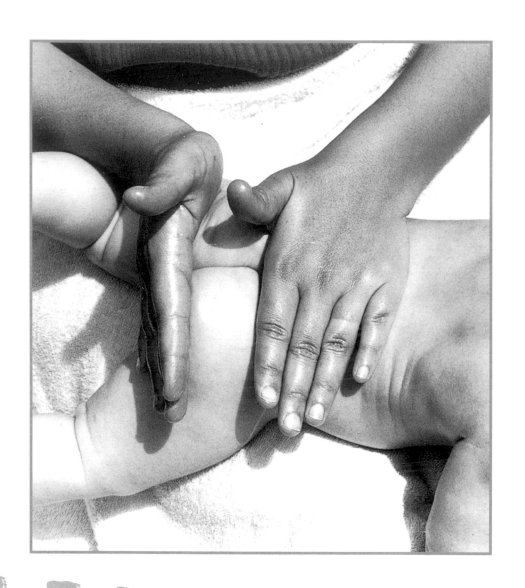

The Back

The spine, along with the back muscles, carry and support the head and act as a support to the chest, abdomen and internal organs. Nerves emerge from between each vertebra of the spine, and connect to different parts of the body. These connections allow us to move and to feel, as well as enabling different body systems to function. The strength and flexibility of the back facilitates deep, relaxed breathing and influences the proper functioning of the internal organs. From the first day of life outside the womb, your baby strengthens his back muscles by trying to lift up his head, and by moving it from side to side while lying down. Later on he does the same while trying to crawl, sit or stand up. When his back muscles are strong enough, he will be able to walk and run. Keeping the back muscles flexible and relaxed from an early age can prevent many posture related problems later on in life.

From the Lower Back to the Hands

The following two sequences, which open this chapter on back massage, are similar to those at the beginning of the chapter on massaging the front of the body. These opening movements should also be repeated five times, alternating between the palms of the hands and the soles of the feet.

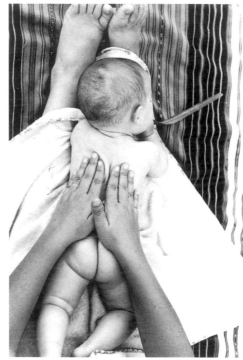

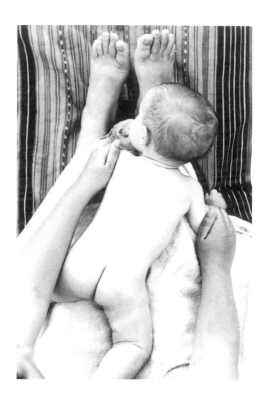

Place your hands on your baby's lower back.

Slide them upwards to the shoulders.

From the shoulders move out along the arms to the fingertips.

From the Lower Back to the Legs

Put a generous amount of oil onto your palms and warm it by rubbing the hands together.

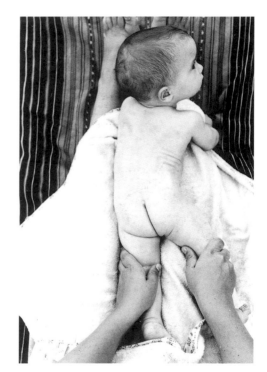

Again place your hands on your baby's lower back.

Slide them up to the shoulders and down along the sides of the body.

Then continue sliding down the hips and the legs all the way to the feet.

Around the Shoulder Blades

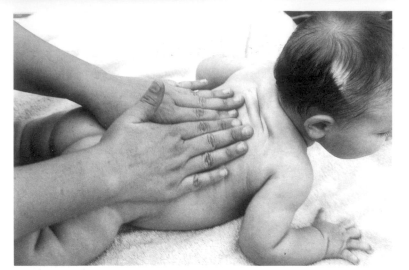

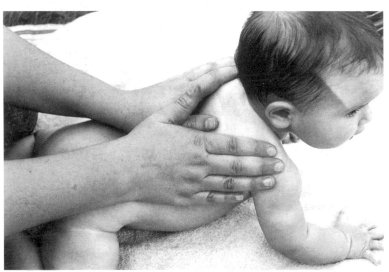

Slide your hands in circular movements around the shoulder blades. Complete about nine circles.

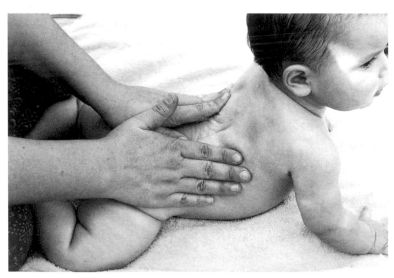

Sliding the Fingers Down the Back

Place your index and middle finger on either side of the top of the spine. Slide them all the way down to the tip of the tail bone, one hand following the other. Gradually increase the pressure and make sure the rhythm is constant. Repeat about nine times.

Palms Along the Back

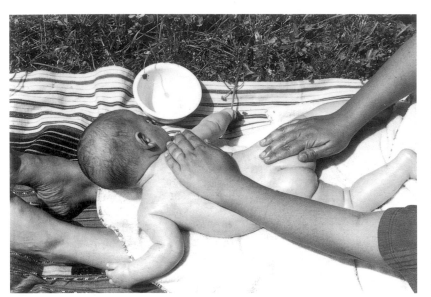 

Slide your palms, one following behind the other down the baby's back. Maintain a slow, calm, steady rhythm.

Sliding the Hands across the Back

Place the palms of your hands in the middle of the baby's back, on both sides of his spine. Slide them out sideways, as if you wanted to flatten out the pages of an open book.

Repeat this movement across the shoulder blades, the middle of the back, and finally the lower back. Repeat the sequence about five times.

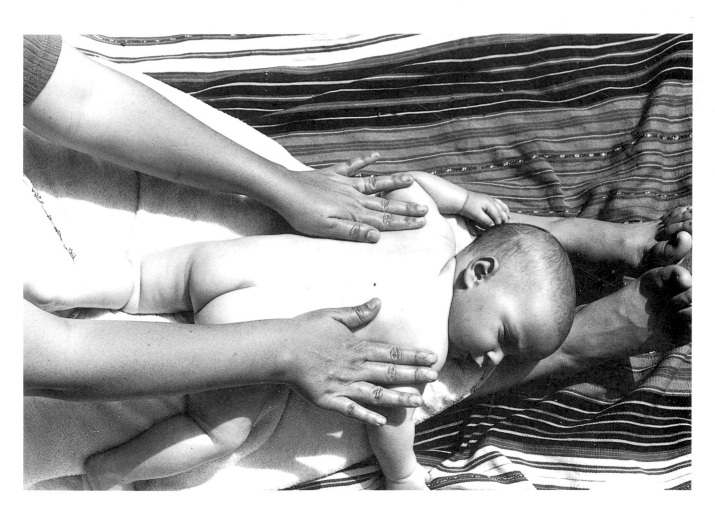

Massaging the Buttocks

With your thumbs, massage the baby's buttocks in wide circular movements.

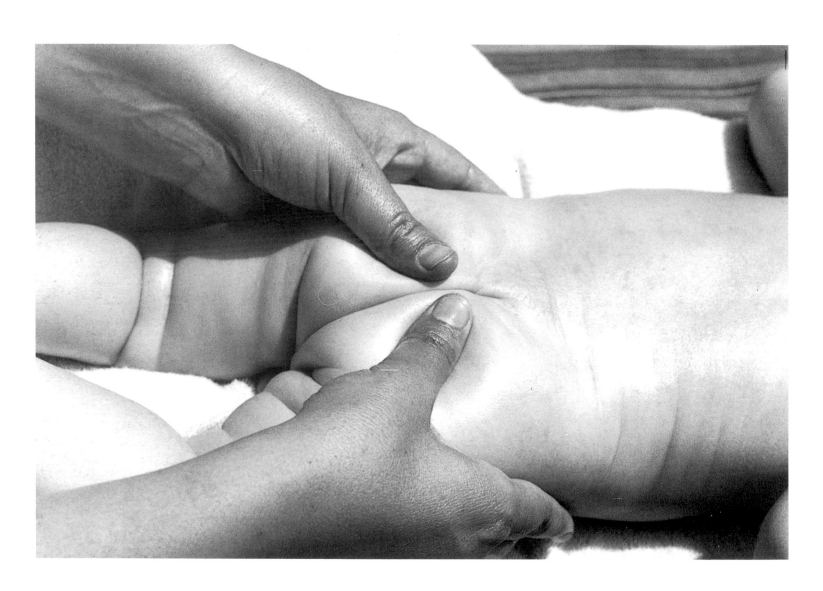

Circular Back Massage

With the palm of your hand, massage the baby's lower back in circular movements. Continue the stroke up to the area between the shoulder blades, and back down again to the lower back. Repeat a few times.

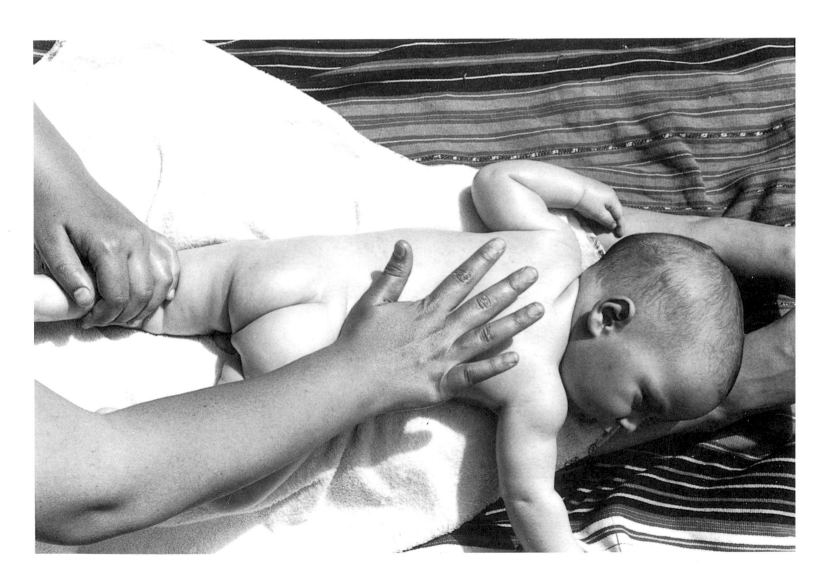

Massaging the Shoulders

Place your hands on the front of the baby's shoulders when he is lying on his front.

Slide them over the top of the shoulders and down along the back.

Stroking across the Back

Place your palms parallel to each other on the baby's upper back. Slide each hand towards and past the other across the back, then reverse the movement, sliding the hands around to the sides of the body. Repeat this movement a few times, up and down the whole back.

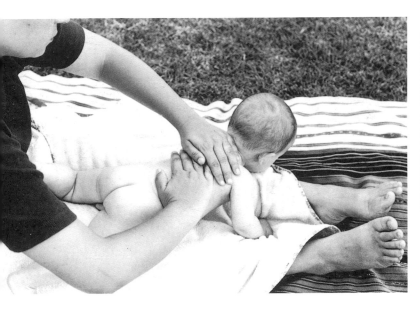

The movement of hands in and out should create folds in the baby's skin, due to the pressure of the hands towards each other.

Make sure your hands are well oiled to ensure a smooth and continuous movement.

Tapping on the Back

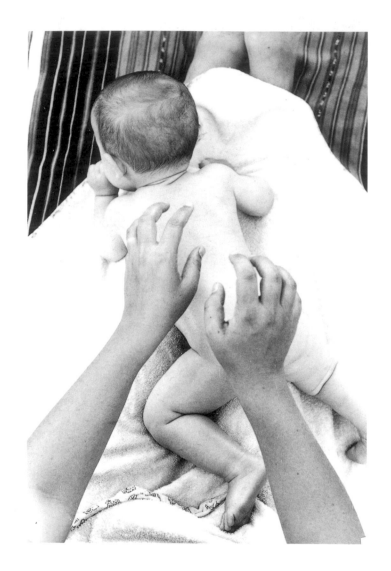

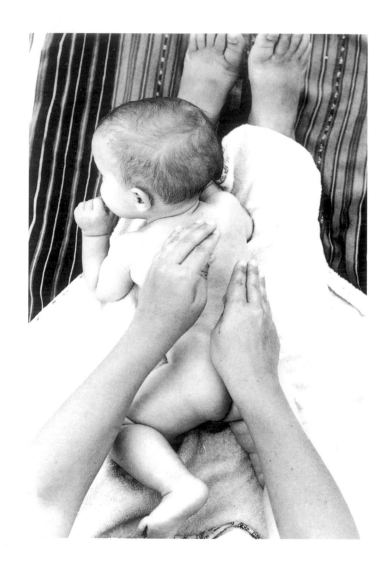

With the fingertips, tap lightly on the baby's back and buttocks.

Then tap these areas with a firm but relaxed cupped hand.

Sliding the Hands Down the Back

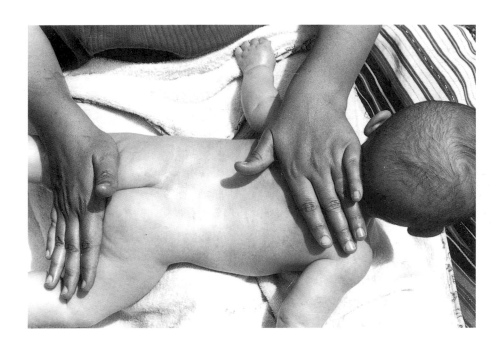

Place one hand on the upper back and the other on the base of the buttocks.

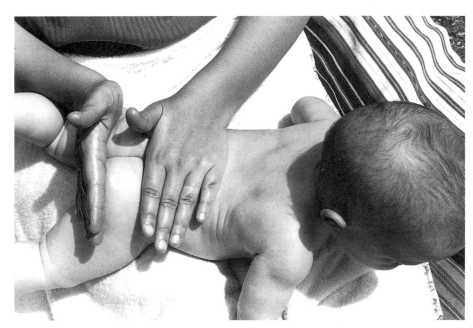

Slide the upper hand down, along the back. Press the buttocks lightly between your hands

Massaging a Baby who is Sitting or Learning to Sit

Massaging the legs and back while the baby is sitting helps the baby to settle into the sitting position by improving her balance and relaxing the hip joints and the leg muscles. If your baby still cannot sit by herself then support her with one hand across her chest and massage her with your other hand.

A Straight movement Down the Back

With a straight movement slide your palms along the baby's spine, from top to bottom, one hand following after the other.

If your baby is not sitting on her own, support her with one hand on the chest and the second sliding down the back.

A Circular Movement along the Back

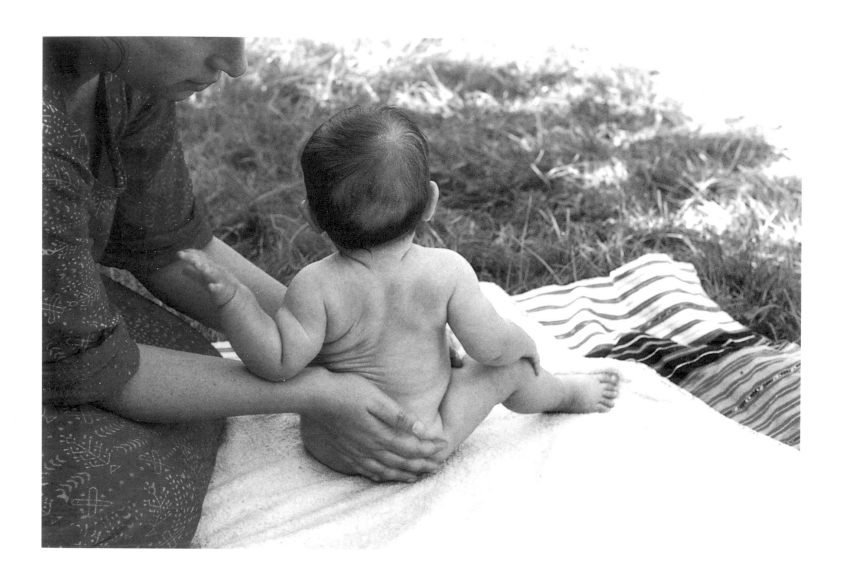

Slide the palm of your hand around in a circular movement, moving from the lower back up as far as the area between the shoulder blades and down again. Support the baby with the other hand holding the front of the body.

The Legs

When the baby is sitting, massage the legs in a squeezing movement from the thighs to the feet.

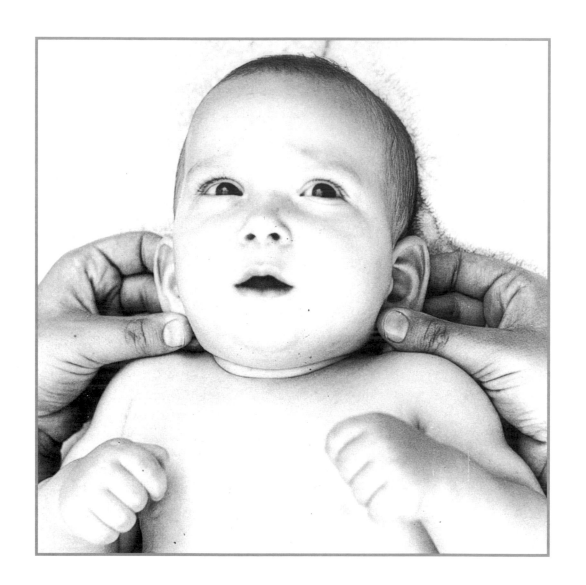

The Face

If you have ever experienced a face massage, either as part of a whole body massage or simply as part of a beauty treatment, you can probably recall how relaxing and pleasant it feels. The face expresses our inner feelings. Inner happiness and peace express themselves in a calm gaze and a shining face. Stress, fear and anger contract the face, especially around the forehead and mouth. If these feelings continue over a period of time, wrinkles can develop.

Massaging babies faces, apart from being fun and relaxing, may help in relieving conditions such as a blocked nose or congested sinuses. If practised regularly it can also help relieve teething problems.

Some babies do not like their faces being touched. If your baby is among them, wait for a while, and try again from time to time. As the baby grows older he is likely to change his likes and dislikes.

Face massage requires very little oil. Take special care around the eyes.

The Forehead

Using your thumbs, stroke the baby's forehead from between the eyebrows ('the third eye') to the crown of the head, one thumb following after the other.

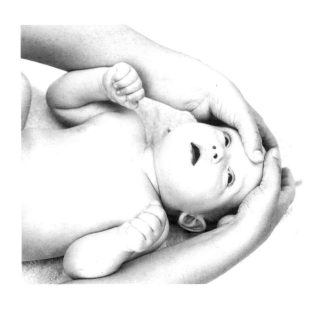

Then place your thumbs in the centre of the forehead, and slide them simultaneously outwards to the temples.

The Cheeks and the Chin

Place your thumbs on the inner side of the cheekbones, near the nose and slide them down along the cheeks, to the jaw bone, while lightly stretching the skin.

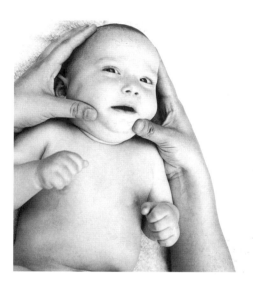

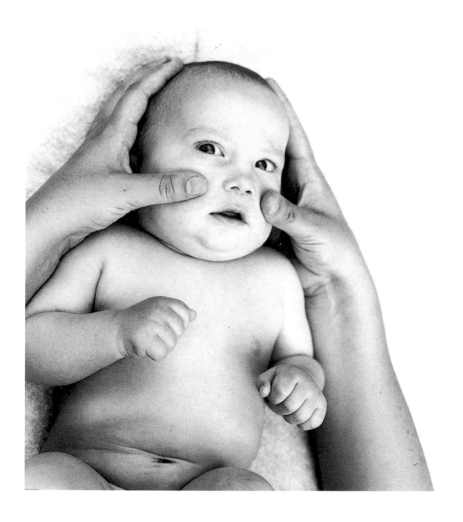

Place the thumbs on the middle of the chin and slide them towards the ears, along the jaw bone.

The Nose

For a blocked nose, place your thumbs on both sides of the nose, at eye level, and press them lightly towards each other. Move down along the nose to the nostrils. The aim of this movement is to clear the accumulation of mucous in the nostrils and sinuses.

The Ears

Place your fingers behind the baby's ears. With your thumbs, gently straighten the folds of the outer ear, massaging them and pulling the lobes downward.

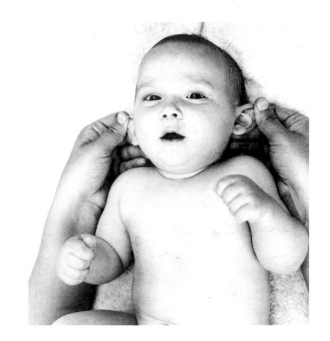

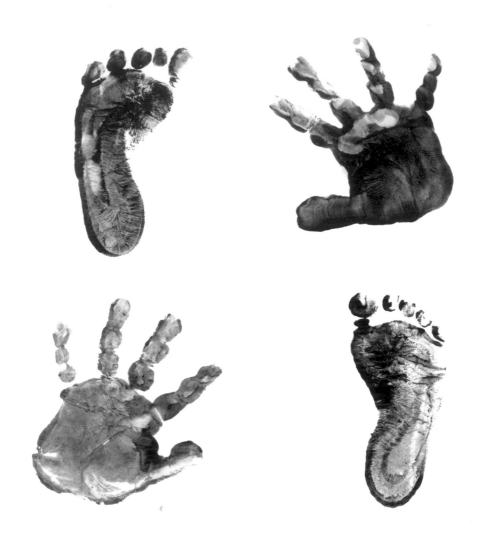

Gymnastics for Babies & Toddlers

Gymnastics plays an important role in flexing the joints, including the hip, knee and shoulder joints. It aids flexibility of the chest and back, thereby improving breathing. Co-ordination is greatly enhanced by this activity, making it beneficial when the baby starts rolling over, crawling and walking.

Gym exercises should be playful: increase the pace, accompany them with songs and rhymes and have fun! As you do this, be attentive to your baby, watch his ability to perform the exercises, and how much he enjoys them. Don't force them on him. If a baby cries or shows discomfort during an exercise, decrease the stretching immediately. These exercises are not suitable for babies under two months old. Allow them to get used to the massage first, and only then gently and gradually incorporate gymnastic exercise into the massage routine.

The exercises can form part of the whole massage or be carried out separately at any time. The baby may be dressed or naked.

Arms In and Out

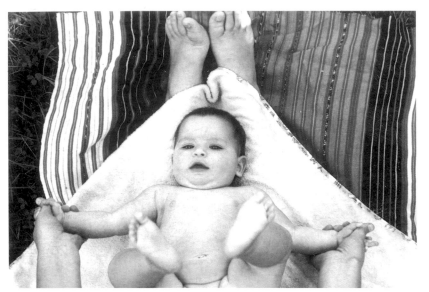 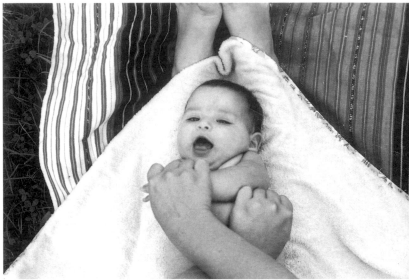

Hold the baby's palms. Pull them out to the sides, and straighten the arms while opening them out, as wide as the baby allows you to. Pause there for a while.

Cross the arms inward, as far as possible, holding them against the chest. Repeat about five times.

A combination of the two movements opens the chest and widens the shoulder blade area.

Arms Up and Down

Take the arms down to the sides of the baby's body. Gently, stretch and straighten them.

Now take the arms upwards, and straighten them above the baby's head. Repeat a few times.

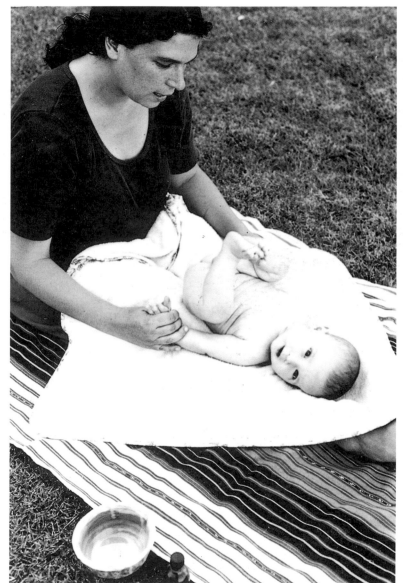

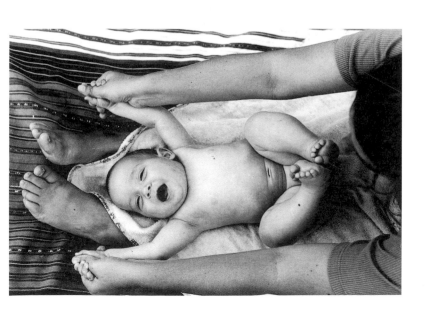

Arms Up and Down Alternately

Lift one of the baby's arms up above his head. Move the other arm down by the side of his body. Now swap arms - the one stretched down goes up and vice versa. Repeat a few times. Make sure both arms are straight during the exercise.

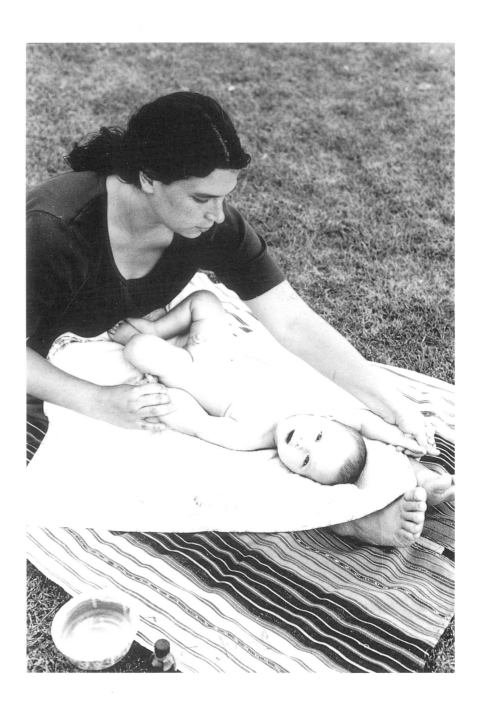

Bending the Legs Alternately

Fold one of the baby's legs and bring it up to the abdomen. The other leg should be straightened and pulled toward you slightly. Change legs. Repeat a few times.

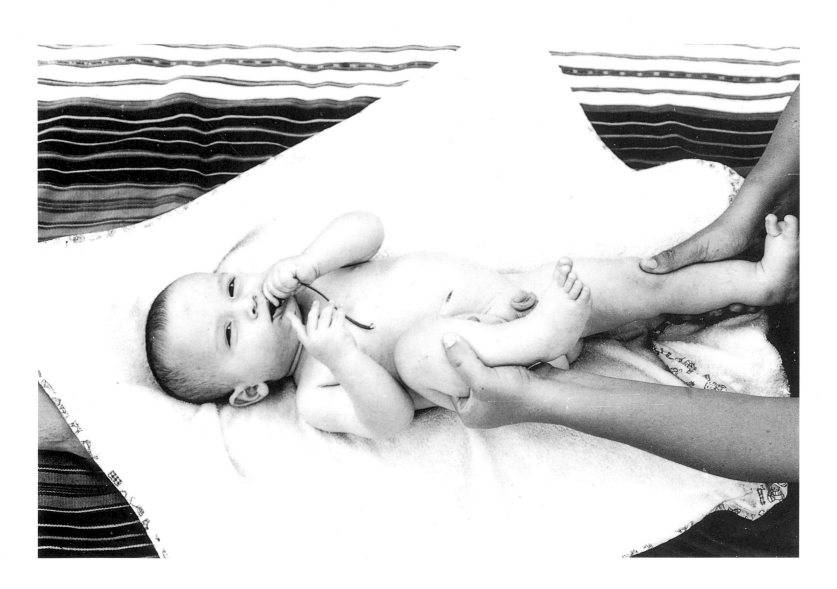

Straightening the Legs

Straighten the baby's legs, and pull them towards you slightly.

Alternate this movement with the next one.

Folding Legs to the Abdomen

Hold the baby's legs with your hands beneath the knees and bring them together. Then flex them so as to bring the knees up to the abdomen, creating gentle pressure on it.

These two movements are especially useful for releasing wind and easing stomach ache.

Feet Together and to the Abdomen

Bring the baby's feet together and by flexing the knees bring them close to the abdomen, knees falling outwards. Gently, swing the legs from side to side.

Bringing Big Toes to Nose

Hold the baby's ankles with both hands. Slowly and gently bring each of the big toes to the face so as to touch the baby's nose, forehead or ears. Repeat few times.

Crossing the legs

Hold the baby's ankles and cross them above the abdomen, (as if in the lotus position). Release the legs and then cross them again, but with the legs reversed. Repeat the movement a few times.

Stretching the Arms Back

With your baby facing down hold the arms behind his back with the palms turned to face each other. Pull them gently so the chest and head will lift above the floor. Release and repeat about three times.

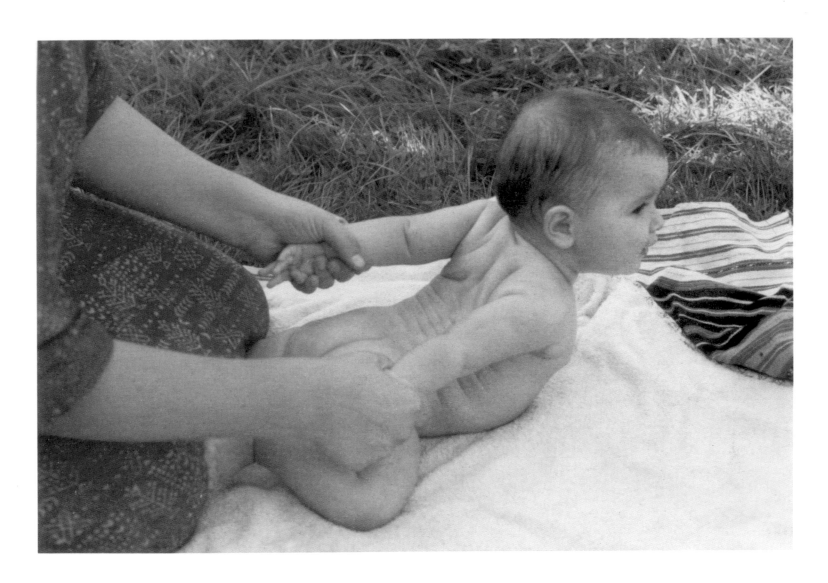

Massaging Older Children

Massaging older children is not different to massaging babies except that more pressure and stretching can be applied.

Older children have less patience to lie still for long, so rather than attempting a full body massage, choose their favourite movements. Accompany these movements with songs, stories and games.

Every parent of a new born baby has an opinion on how they would like to raise their child; what to do or not to do; how and why. These philosophies may be taken from a variety of books on bringing up children and child psychology, or from suggestions and experiences of family and friends, as well as memories of their own childhood. Ideas vary considerably but as a rule parents love their children and will do everything they can to facilitate their happiness.

When I was pregnant with my first son a friend gave me the book 'The Continuum Concept' by Jean Liedloff. I found it very helpful, as it opened a window into a world that I felt we had grown so far a way from, one in which I believe we all have our roots. A world which is natural to human nature and primal expectations, not one where conflicting theories from so called experts are the result of scientific evidence and are so often opposed to natural instincts. Jean Liedloff spent five years living in South America with the Yequana tribe,

where she studied their ways, especially in relation to bringing up children. Her main observation of that which is so obviously different from the so - called civilized world, was the constant physical contact between the mother, or other adults and the baby. During the day the child would be close to his mother, attached to her by a sling, and during the night the baby always slept next to her, being fed on demand. Constant physical contact and demand feeding are the absolute expectations of a new born baby. From the moment of birth, if fulfilled they represent a natural progression from pre-natal life. Liedloff followed the growth of these babies and noticed that not only did they cry less and not suffer from colic pain, but they grew to be confident, physically co-ordinated and flexible, and emotionally stable toddlers, children and adults.

Jean Liedloff's research has guided us in bringing up our three children, although I have to admit that we found it difficult carrying them as babies throughout the entire day due to our daily routine and lack of support through not living within a commune. However we maintained physical contact as much as possible. My husband would often hold the baby while working at home, or when relaxing. We would also have the baby with us at mealtimes, bath-times, when sleeping, and of course the time we spent giving a massage. Our first son slept with us from the moment he was born, after 18 months our second son joined us too, one on each side of the bed. We only moved them into a room of their own when I was expecting our daughter.

Human touch is a necessity for babies, children, adults and the elderly. It is relaxing, reassuring, it gives a sense of security, warmth and self esteem. It is the physical expression of love! This is what this book is about. As the children grow up I see that when they come home from school after a long day and are unhappy, often all they need is a long comforting hug and instantly their mood changes.

I have no doubt that all couples have their own ideas. What is good for one family might not suit another. That is when parents need to follow their own instincts in order to find the best approach for their family. It is not necessary to follow what the so called 'experts' say (that includes this book), unless it makes complete sense to you.

Regarding massage, as the children become older I have found that it has opened a door to a wider communication, not only between me and the children but between the children themselves. Now when we give a massage it is a "family event" as the three of them lay on the bed next to each other enjoying the tingling sensation of the oil and hands on their bodies. Often one of them will help me to massage the others and sometimes I even get a little rub!

They have learned to ask for a massage whenever they have a stomach-ache or if they feel unwell, and I often use it when they have a cold or cough; when they are constipated or just feeling tired and upset.

The extent to which massage has become part of my family's life has gone beyond my expectations and imagination from the time when I first started massaging my eldest son to relieve his colic pain and to relax him and myself. I hope to see the children using massage throughout their lives including on their own children.

I hope this book will inspire you and will bring back the use of massage in the family throughout generations to come.

Galit Hughes

About the Author

Galit graduated as an acupuncturist and massage therapist from the International College of Oriental Medicine in 1994. It was whilst at college that she met her husband Rob. They now have three children who have all benefited from regular massage since birth.

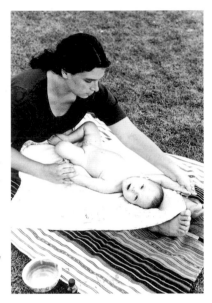

Galit had previously studied dance and yoga in Israel. Further studies in England have enabled her to bring together her clinical and mothering experience in the form of a series of workshops designed to teach parents how and when to massage their babies and children. She has guided many parents in both England and Israel.

Galit currently shares her time between her acupuncture practice, teaching massage at the International College of Oriental Medicine, running baby massage workshops and being with the family.

A Hebrew edition of the book is currently being published in Israel.

An easy to follow guide, this book presents a highly readable manual of baby massage. It is designed with first-time and experienced parents, grandparents, as well as health workers and therapists in mind. A baby or child receiving regular massage will benefit from the following:

+ Relief from colic, colds, coughs, irritability, sleeplessness and more.
+ Strengthening of the immune system and improving the circulation of blood.
+ Enhancing co-ordination and flexibility.

Regular massage has been shown to ease post-natal depression, increase confidence within the family and deepen love and communication between massage provider and child. A book to be referred to for years to come and enjoyed by friends and family alike.

This is an excellent book! A clear, concise guide with beautifully presented photographs, I would recommend it to all parents interested in deepening the bond with their children in both a loving and therapeutic way. With just a little time and application, it is possible to learn simple skills whereby your baby or child can be enabled to feel good in his or her body as well as benefiting from the alleviation of straightforward symptoms such as a cold or colic. For parents this can be immensely rewarding and empowering, knowing that you are more equipped to respond to your child's needs, both emotional and physical.

Diane Jones BAc.   Acupuncturist, body worker and mother.

SHUNYATA

DESIGN by Sarit Zeltzer

ISBN 0-95   3

9 780954 014308